Lolly Sticks

You will need four different-sized lolly sticks to make the projects in this book. Each project will tell you which size you need. This is how they are described throughout ...

small lolly stick

medium lolly stick

large lolly stick

XL lolly stick

Lolly sticks shown to scale.

Top tips

• Keep a handy store of crafting materials: felt, coloured tissue paper, card or paper, wool, string, ribbon, fuzzy sticks, beads, sequins, plastic gems and buttons are all useful.

• Keep any offcuts of felt and fabric. These come in handy for the snowmen.

• Clothes pegs work as clamps to hold lolly sticks together while the glue dries.

You will need

- 5 large lolly sticks
- Tracing paper · Pencil
- Glue · Clothes pegs
- Paint · Paintbrush
- Coloured glitter
- A plastic container or dish
- Ribbon (optional)

4

★ Shimmering Stars ★

These simple shimmering stars look great
as Christmas decorations!

1 You need to arrange five lolly sticks into a star shape. This is quite tricky so trace the template on page 32 and use this to build your star on. It will help you to get the angles right.

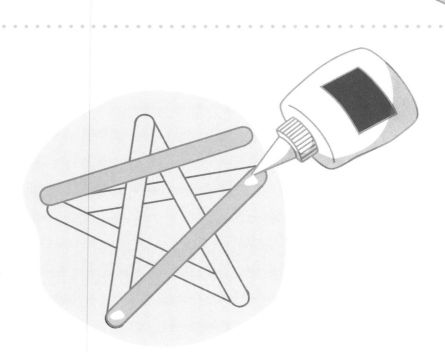

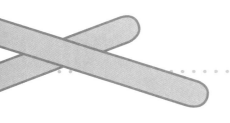

2 Begin by placing one lolly stick on the star template, then apply a blob of glue on each end. Lay the second stick on the template, carefully placing one end over the blob of glue.

3 Apply a blob of glue on the second stick and carefully lay the third stick on, as shown.

4 Now apply a blob of glue on the third stick and carefully lay the fourth stick on.

5 Repeat with the fifth stick. The best way to get your star to stick is to pinch each joint together with a clothes peg, as shown, and allow to dry.

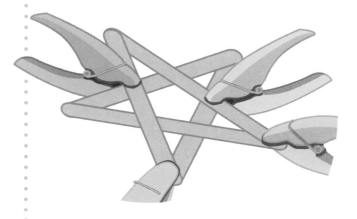

6 Once the glue is dry, remove the pegs and paint the star a colour which will match the glitter you want to use. Allow to dry.

7 When the paint is dry, coat the star with a thin layer of glue. Place in a container and carefully sprinkle with glitter, ensuring you cover it completely. Shake the loose glitter off and allow to dry.

8 When your star is dry it is ready to display. Why not tie a ribbon through one of the points to hang it.

You will need
• 4 XL lolly sticks
• Pencil and ruler
• Clothes pegs
• Ribbon or string
• Scissors • Glue
• Paint • Paintbrush
• Beads • Buttons
or gems

Picture Frames

These sweet picture frames
make great gifts!

1 Take four XL lolly
sticks. Measure 2 cm
from both ends of each stick
and mark with a pencil.

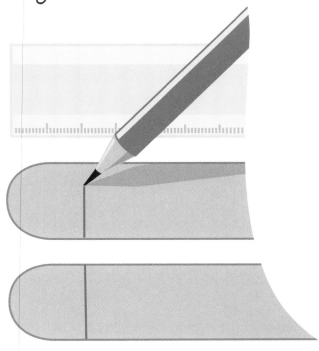

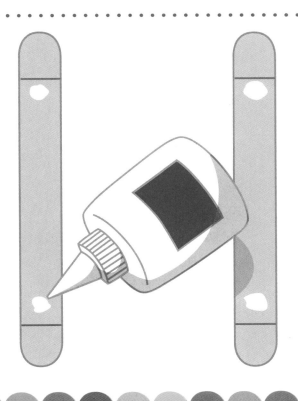

2 Lay two of the sticks
vertically, side by side,
about 7 cm apart. Apply a blob
of glue inside each marked
line, as shown.

3 Place the two remaining sticks horizontally, on top of the two vertical sticks, lining up the pencil marks.

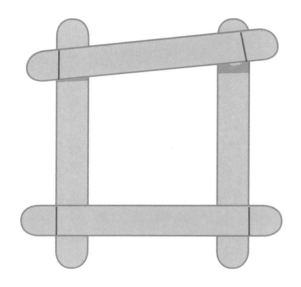

4 Using clothes pegs, nip each corner together, and leave to dry.

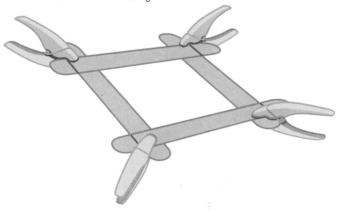

5 Once the glue is dry, remove the pegs and paint the frame. Leave to dry.

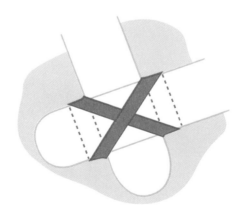

6 Now you are ready to add the final decorations to your frame. Use the ribbon or string to tie crosses on the two bottom corners. Keep the knots on the reverse of the frame.

7 With a longer length of ribbon or string, tie a cross in one top corner, thread beads on to create a hanger, then knot onto the final corner of the sticks, lining up the pencil marks.

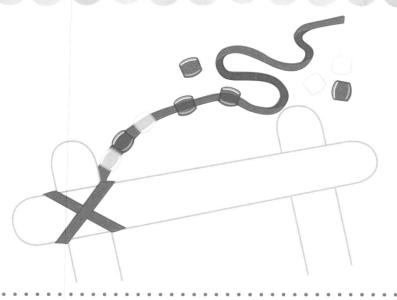

8 Glue on buttons or gems to make your frame look really special.

9 Now you are ready to frame your favourite pictures!

You will need

- 6 XL lolly sticks
- 1 small lolly stick
- Scissors • Glue
- Clothes pegs
- Paint: white, black and red • Paintbrush
- Goggly eyes • Button
- Black felt-tip pen

TOP TIP

If you don't have goggly eyes, make them from card, or paint the eyes on instead.

Spot the Dog

This playful pup is fun to
make and looks cute!

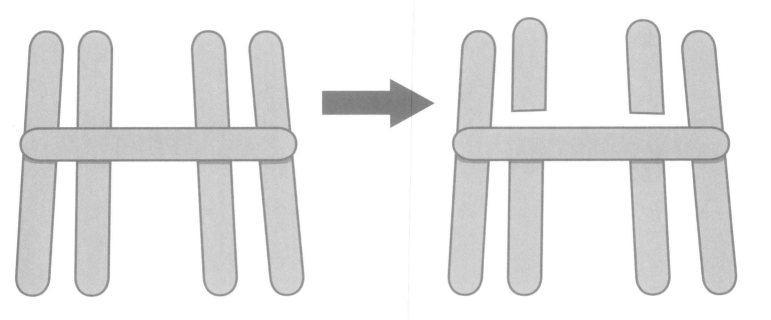

1 Arrange five XL lolly
sticks to form the dog's
body and legs, as shown above.
You will need to trim the
two middle sticks (keep the
offcuts to make the ears).
Leave the left-hand and
right-hand sticks complete.

2 Glue the lolly sticks in
place, and leave to dry.

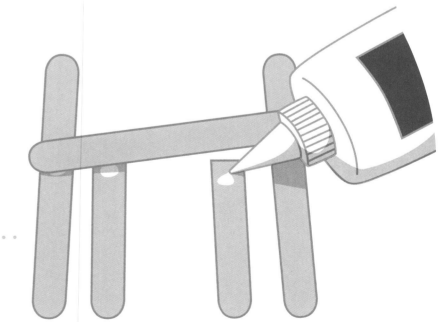

3 To build the head, cut the remaining XL lolly stick into three pieces.

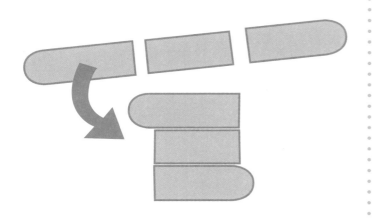

4 Glue the three head pieces onto the right-hand lolly stick, as shown.

5 Once the glue has dried, paint the dog white. Leave to dry.

6 Make the ears out of the leg offcuts, from step 1. Trim them at an angle, as shown. Paint the ears black and leave to dry.

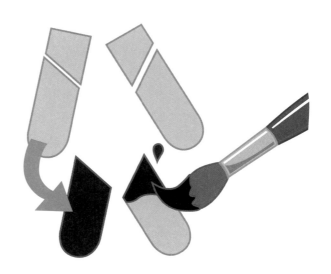

7 Use the black paint to add Spot's spots!

8 Next, take the small lolly stick and trim each end to create Spot's collar. Paint this red and allow to dry.

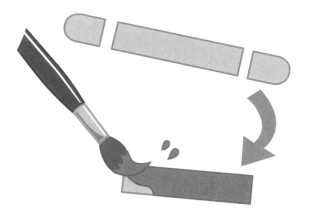

9 Glue the ears and collar onto the head. Use a black felt-tip pen to add Spot's eye patch.

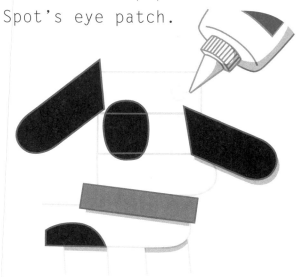

10 Finish your playful pup by adding a black button nose, whiskers and a smiling mouth.

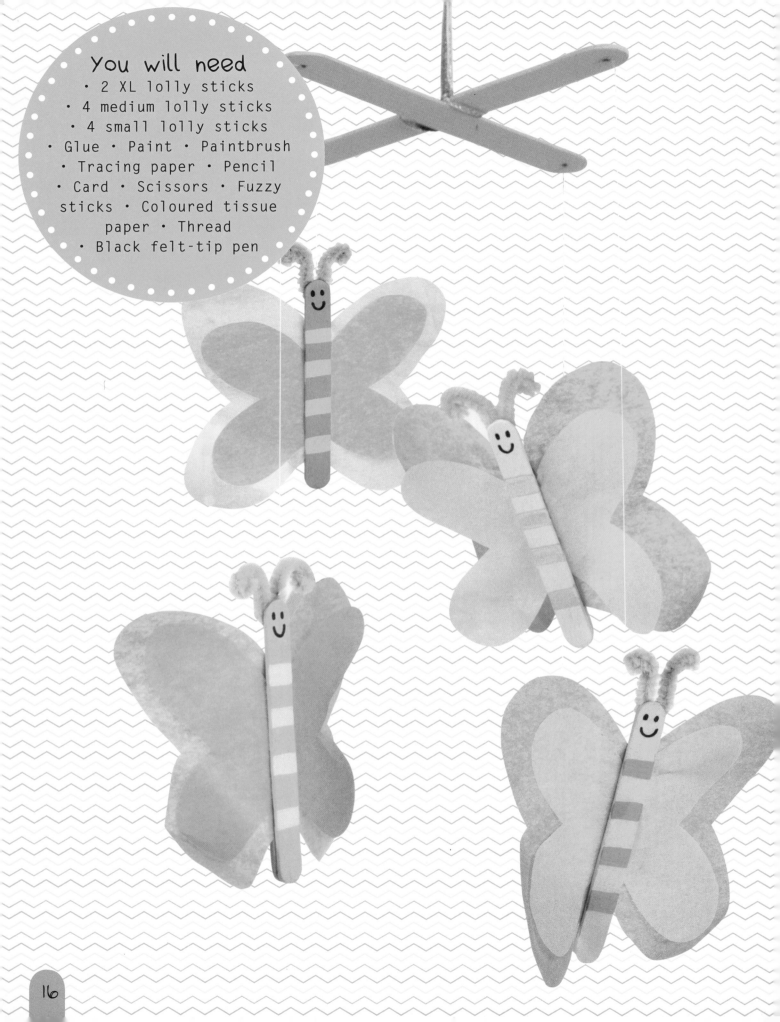

You will need
- 2 XL lolly sticks
- 4 medium lolly sticks
- 4 small lolly sticks
- Glue • Paint • Paintbrush
- Tracing paper • Pencil
- Card • Scissors • Fuzzy
sticks • Coloured tissue
paper • Thread
- Black felt-tip pen

16

Butterfly Mobile

Make these fantastic flutterers come alive!

1 Paint the four medium and four small lolly sticks in different pastel shades, in pairs, and allow to dry. You can make pastel shades by mixing a darker colour with white.

2 Next, paint contrasting stripes on each of these sticks. Leave a space approx 2 cm long, on the medium sticks, for the faces. Allow to dry.

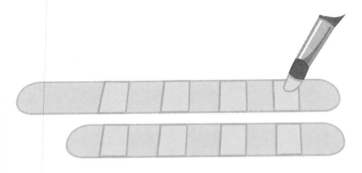

3 Cut fuzzy sticks into 3 cm lengths to make four pairs of antennae. Glue to the back of each medium lolly stick.

4 Once dry, use the black felt-tip pen to draw faces on the front. Set these aside.

5 Now get the two XL lolly sticks. Apply a blob of glue in the centre of one and position the remaining stick on top to create a cross shape. Once the glue is dry, paint pale green all over.

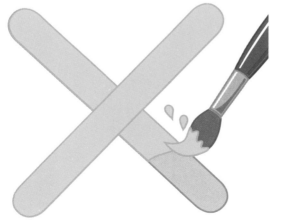

6 To create the wings, trace the two templates on page 32 onto card and cut out carefully.

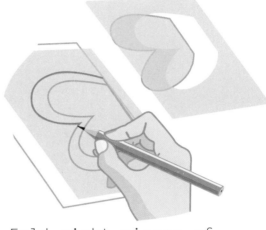

7 Fold eight pieces of different-coloured tissue paper in half. On four, place the big template as shown, draw around it and cut out the shape. Repeat on the other pieces using the smaller template.

Place template on fold

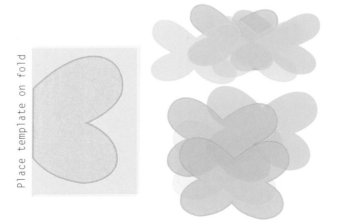

8 Cut four lengths of thread about 40 cm long. Take the four small lolly sticks and tie thread about 2 cm from the end of each stick.

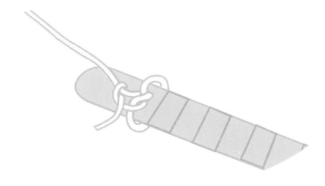

9 Assemble the butterflies as shown below, building up each layer with a little glue.

Small stick

Large wing

Small wing

Medium stick

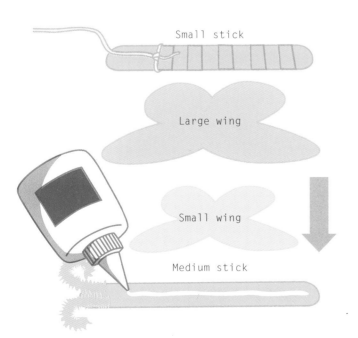

10 Tie one butterfly to each end of the green cross, adjusting the lengths so they all hang at slightly different heights. Secure with a blob of glue. Attach a ribbon to the centre of the cross and ask an adult to help hang it from the ceiling.

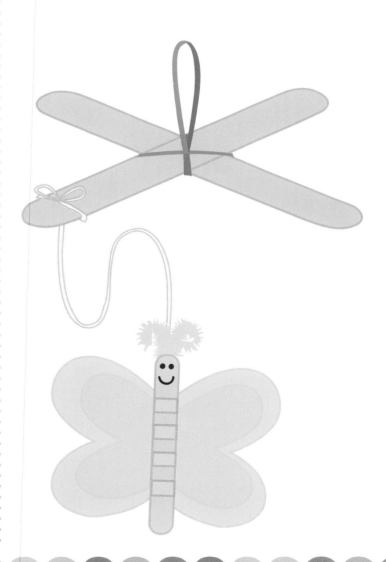

You will need

• 7 medium lolly sticks
• 9 small lolly sticks
• 1 large lolly stick
• Glue • Modelling clay
• Paint • Coloured paper
• White button
• Scissors
• Paintbrush

Sailing Boat

Set sail for the high seas with this smart sailing boat.

1 Cut one of the seven medium lolly sticks in half and trim a tiny bit off each straight piece, as shown. Set aside.

2 Arrange the nine small lolly sticks side by side. Use a straight edge to line up the sticks.

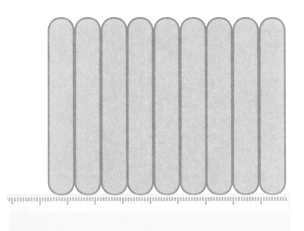

3 Apply a thin line of glue along each stick.

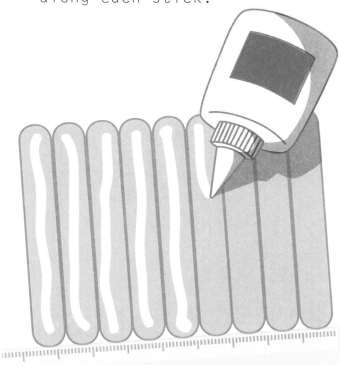

4 Place the seven medium lolly sticks, one by one, across the nine small sticks. The one you cut in half must go in the middle, leaving a gap, as shown. Let the glue dry.

5 Take the remaining large lolly stick and trim the end off to create a straight edge.

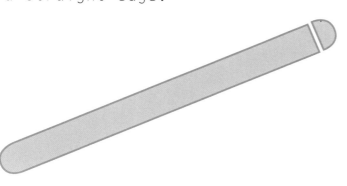

6 Position this lolly stick vertically in the gap left on the base of the boat. Glue in place. Whilst this dries, it is a good idea to support it with some modelling clay.

7 Once this is dry, you can paint your boat's hull and mast.

8 Out of a piece of coloured paper, cut a triangle about 9 cm high. Cut two slits in the triangle, as shown.

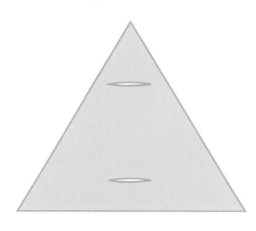

10 For a finishing touch, paint a button white. Leave it to dry, then paint the edge red leaving four white stripes to create a life ring. You could use a circle of cardboard if you don't have a button. You're ready to set sail!

9 Carefully slide the sail onto the mast of your boat.

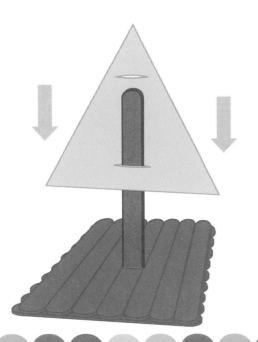

You will need
- 4 XL lolly sticks
- 1 small lolly stick • Glue
- Paint • Paintbrush • Scissors
- Paper • Scraps of felt
- Buttons, pompoms, fuzzy sticks and sequins
- Black paper • Card
- Red ribbon and string
- Black felt-tip pen

Jolly Snowmen

Do you wanna build a snowman?
Perfect decorations for the Christmas tree!

1 Paint each XL lolly stick white and allow to dry.

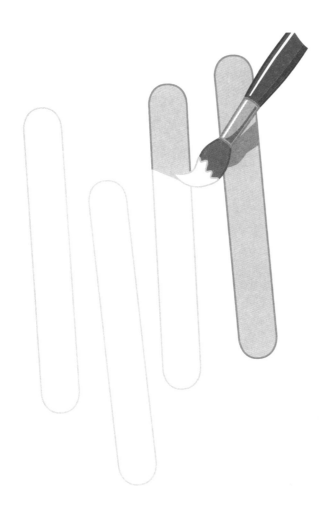

2 To make the snowman with the green hat, take the small lolly stick and glue it across one of the white lolly sticks, about 3 cm from one end. Let it dry and paint the hat shape green.

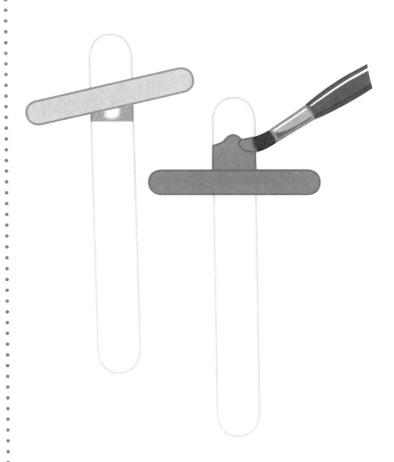

3 Out of a scrap of felt, cut three shapes to form a scarf. Snip the ends of the two smaller ones to create a fringe.

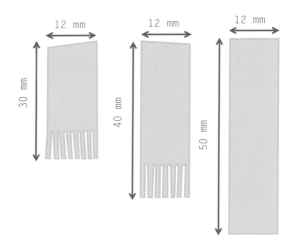

4 Wrap the large piece around the neck of the snowman and glue. Position the other pieces at the angles shown, and glue.

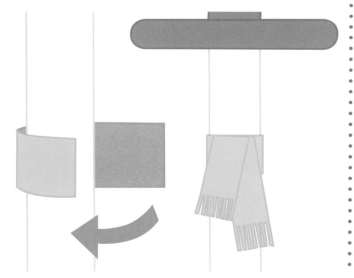

5 Finish decorating this snowman by sticking on a small orange pompom for his nose. Draw his face with a black felt-tip pen, and glue on tiny squares of black paper to make his buttons. Finally, tie red ribbon around his hat to decorate it and create a ribbon hanger.

6 For the red and blue snowman hats, cut out felt in the sizes shown here. Snip the ends of the red felt to create a fringe.

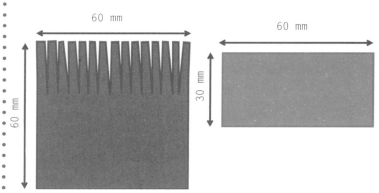

7 Add glue to the top of two sticks and wrap the felt around the tops, as shown. Fold the blue felt corners over to neaten. Leave to dry.

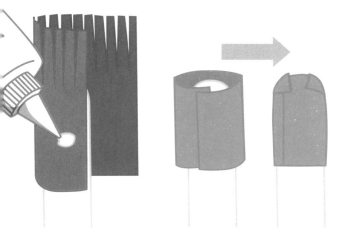

8 Wrap string around the top of the red hat and pull tight, as shown, to form a hanger. Glue string to the back of the blue hat.

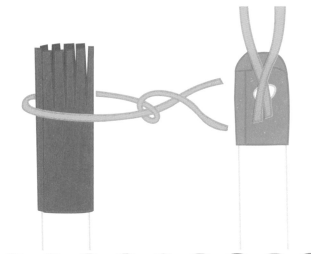

9 Make a top hat out of card and paint it black.

10 To finish your snowmen, create noses, scarves and buttons with ribbon, fuzzy sticks, pompoms, scraps of felt, sequins or buttons. Draw on their faces with a black felt-tip pen. Let your imagination run wild!

You will need
- 1 XL lolly stick
- 2 large lolly sticks
- 2 medium lolly sticks
- 1 small lolly stick
- Glue • Paint • Paintbrush
- Silver card • Scrap of card
- Silver ribbon • Buttons, pompoms, sequins and glitter

28

Christmas Tree

If you're dreaming of a white Christmas, this tree is the perfect creative decoration.

1 Arrange your lolly sticks in the order shown below. Trim 1 cm from one medium stick and 1 cm from one large stick, keeping each end curved to match the uncut ends.

2 Next, glue the sticks to the XL lolly stick 'trunk', as shown, to make a Christmas tree shape.

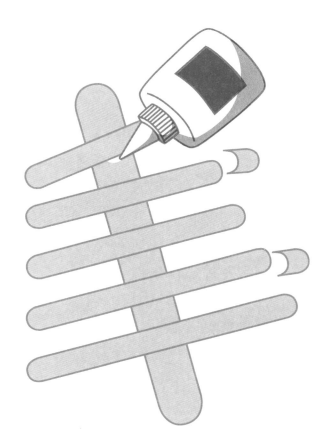

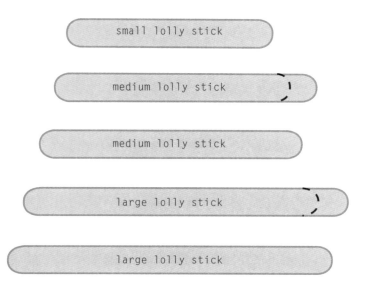

small lolly stick

medium lolly stick

medium lolly stick

large lolly stick

large lolly stick

3 Paint the tree green and allow it to dry.

4 Wrap the silver ribbon around the tree and glue at the back, as shown.

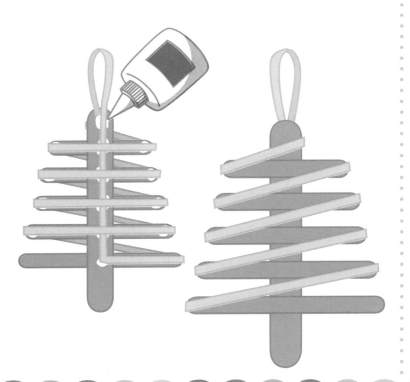

5 Trace these star shapes and use them as templates to cut out stars from silver card. Set aside.

Star templates

6 Now cut out a square of cardboard to make the pot. Cut along the sides and paint it red with white stripes.

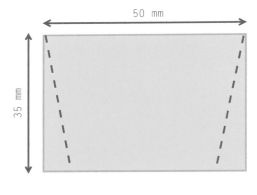

50 mm

35 mm

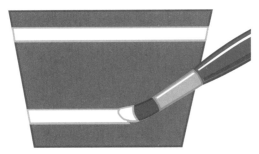

7 Glue the pot to the base of the tree's trunk. Stick the silver stars in place, too.

8 Now you can put the finishing touches to your Christmas tree! Stick on pompoms, buttons, beads, sequins and glitter to make the most beautiful Christmas tree ever!

Templates

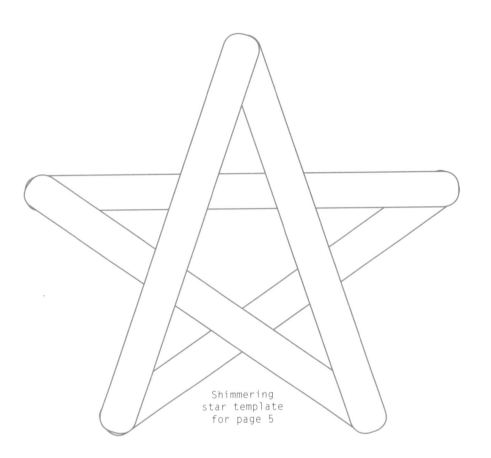

Shimmering
star template
for page 5

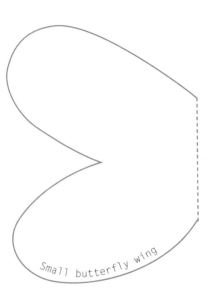

Small butterfly wing

Butterfly wings
templates for page 18

When you've completed the lolly
stick projects in this book,
why not invent some cool craft
creations of your own.

Large butterfly wing